Class Pets

Las mascotas de la clase

by Deborah Schecter

ISBN: 978-1-338-70296-5
Illustrated by Anne Kennedy

Published by Scholastic Inc., 557 Broadway, New York, NY 10012

10 9 8 7 6 68 23 24 25 26/0

Printed in Jiaxing, China. First printing, June 2020.

SCHOLASTIC

The rabbit sniffs
around and around.

El conejo olfatea
dando vueltas sin parar.

The fish swims
around and around.

El pez nada
dando vueltas sin parar.

The mouse crawls
around and around.

El ratón se pasea
dando vueltas sin parar.

The hamster runs
around and around.

El hámster corre
dando vueltas sin parar.

The snake slides
around and around.

La serpiente se arrastra
dando vueltas sin parar.

The frog hops
around and around.

La rana salta
dando vueltas sin parar.

Class pets
all around and around!

¡Las mascotas
dan vueltas sin parar!